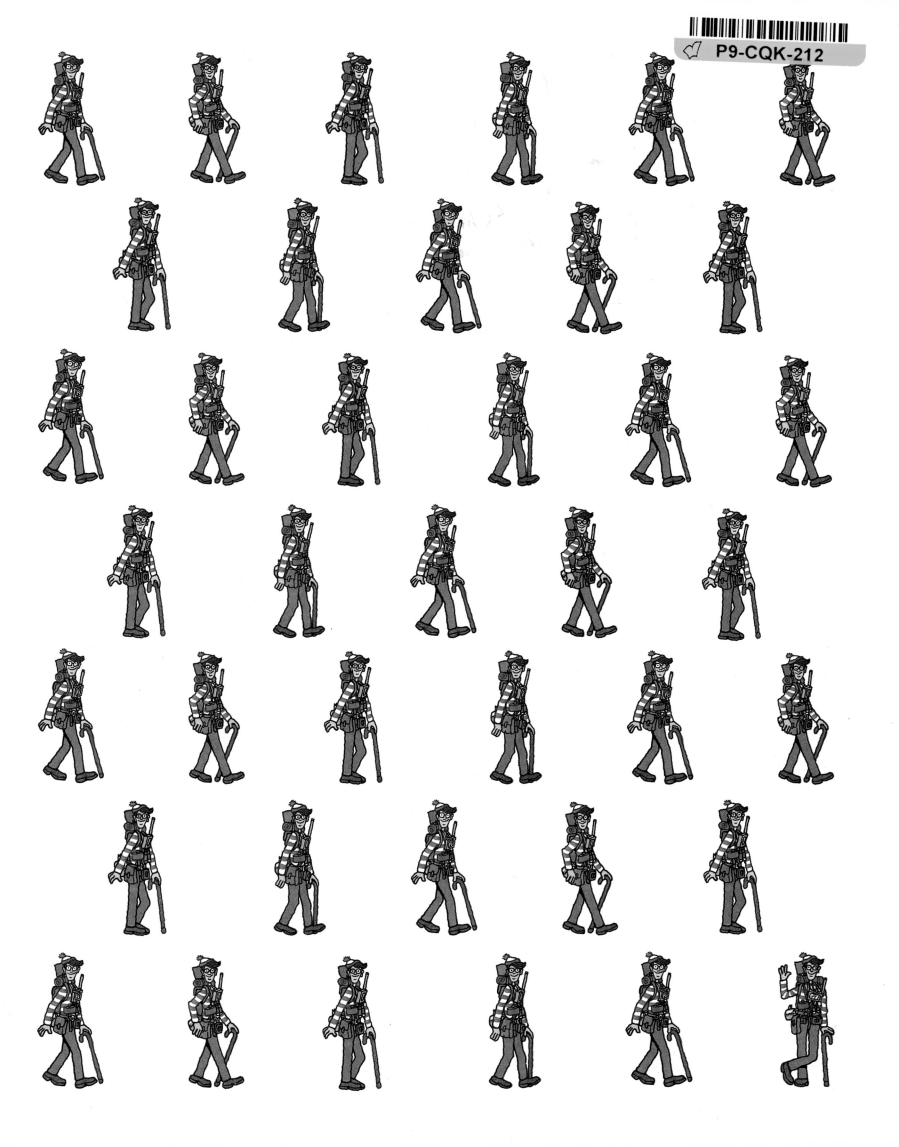

For Wally

First published in Canada
by Grolier Limited, 1987
20 Torbay Road, Markham, Ontario L3R 1G6
Telephone (416) 474-0333

First published 1987
by Walker Books Ltd.
87 Vauxhall Walk, London SE11 5HJ

© 1987 Martin Handford

First printed 1987
Printed and bound by L.E.G.O., Vicenza, Italy

Canadian Cataloguing in Publication Data
Handford, Martin
Where's Waldo?
ISBN 0-7172-2169-5
I. Title.
PZ7.H36Wh 1987   j823'.914   C87-093315-9

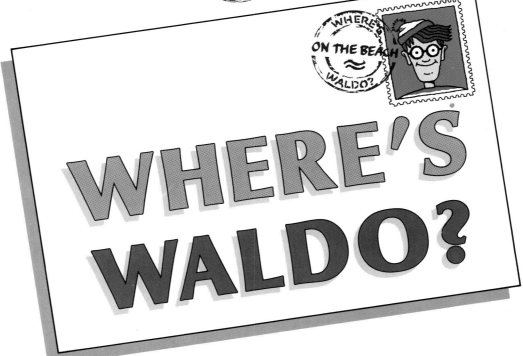

WHERE'S WALDO?

MARTIN HANDFORD

GROLIER LIMITED
TORONTO

HI, FRIENDS!

MY NAME IS WALDO.
I'M JUST SETTING OFF ON A WORLD-
WIDE HIKE. YOU CAN COME TOO.
ALL YOU HAVE TO DO IS FIND ME,
WHEREVER I GO.

I'VE GOT ALL I NEED—WALKING
STICK, KETTLE, MALLET, CUP,
BACKPACK, SLEEPING BAG,
BINOCULARS, CAMERA, SNORKEL,
BELT, BAG AND SHOVEL.

WHEN I WAS IN TOWN TODAY I SAW
LOTS OF INTERESTING THINGS.
A WINDOW CLEANER EVEN DROPPED
A BUCKET ON A MAN'S HEAD.
OUCH!

Waldo

GREETINGS,
WALDO FOLLOWERS!
WOW, THE BEACH WAS
GREAT TODAY! I SAW
THIS GIRL STICK
ICE CREAM IN HER
BROTHER'S FACE, AND
THERE WAS A SAND
CASTLE WITH A REAL
KNIGHT IN ARMOR
INSIDE! FANTASTIC!

Waldo

TO:
WALDO FOLLOWERS,
HERE, THERE,
EVERYWHERE.

WHERE'S
ON THE BEACH
WALDO?

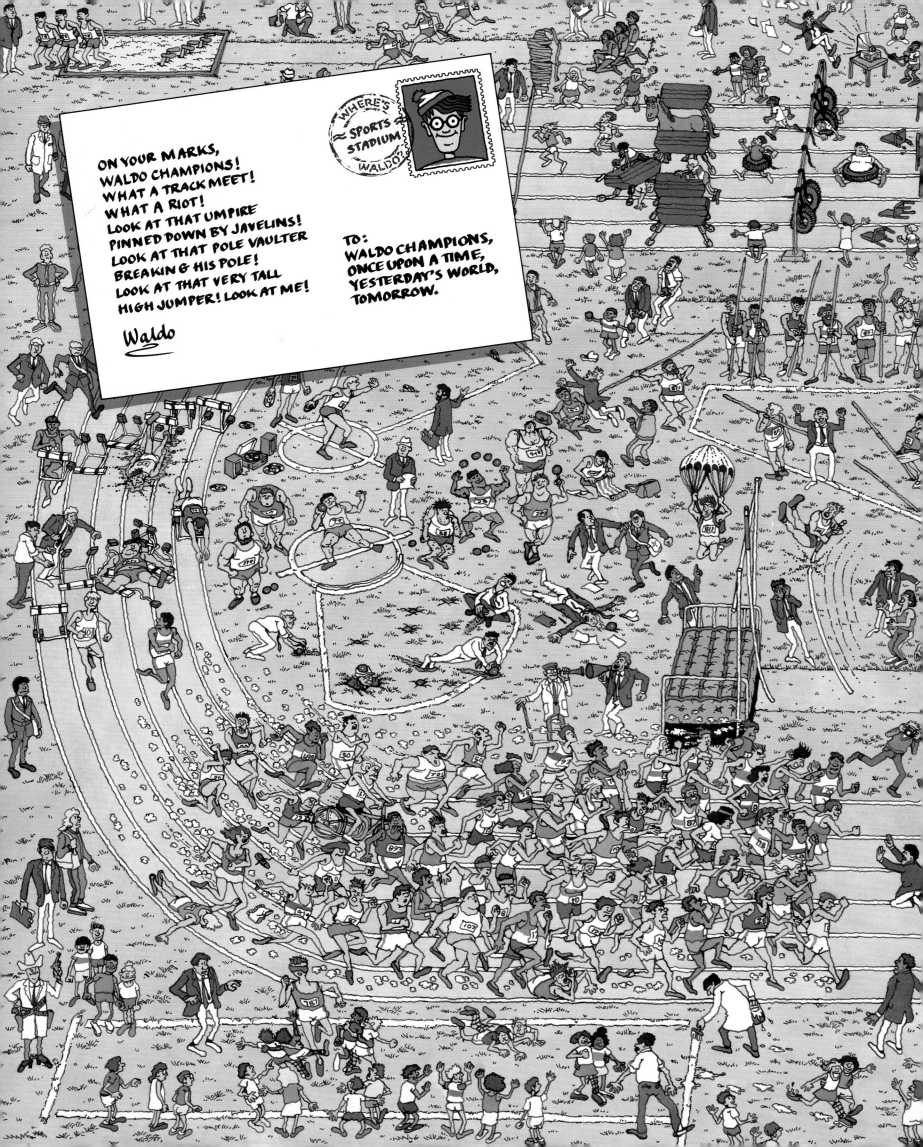